For Conor and Sadhbh
ED and JG

For Kate Janaki (Ella) and Dara Luca
SK

Katie - the facts

The name Catherine, now more popularly adapted as Katie or Kate, probably derived from the Greek Katharos (pure), has many rich historical and religious backgrounds.

Our tale is inspired by Catherine of Alexandria. According to legend the 4th century Egyptian saint denounced the Roman emperor for persecution of Christianity. She then befriended and converted 50 pagan philosophers whom he had assembled to undermine her religion. Having rebuffed all attempts to limit her religious endeavours, she was sentenced to death on a rotating 'Catherine' wheel. This was a medieval device for torture and execution to which condemned persons were attached. More recently it is the name given to a type of revolving firecracker.

Legend records that the device shattered into pieces, saving the saint's life but killing many who came to witness her execution.

Henry VIII's first wife, Catherine of Aragon, also had a stubborn streak. She so successfully resisted the English king's attempts to divorce her, taking her case all the way to Rome, that he forced Parliament to renounce the religious authority of the Vatican, beginning the process of setting up a separate English church.

Two of Henry's other wives shared the name. Catherine Howard was beheaded at the king's command at the age of 20 for deceiving him. His sixth and final wife, Catherine Parr, effectively nursed him during his final illness.

A 14th century Catherine, of Sienna, patron saint of Italy, lived an ascetic religious life while also acting as advisor to rulers both in Italy and the Vatican. She exerted a particular influence over Pope Gregory XI.

Catherine of Breganza, a gambling addict, was accused of attempting to poison her husband, Charles II of England. Catherine de'Medici, Queen of France during the religious wars of the 16th century, played a major part in defending French unity. Catherine of Valois, daughter of the mad Charles VI of England and wife of Henry V, caused political and legislative consternation when she sought to remarry after the king's death.

Catherine I, illiterate and raised as a foundling, married Peter the Great, eventually becoming Empress of Russia on his death in 1725. Catherine II, during a 34 year reign beginning in 1762, greatly expanded Russian territory and influence at the expense of Sweden, Poland and Turkey.

Modern bearers of the name include Katherine Hepburn, Catherine Zeta Jones, Catherine Deneveuve, Kate Moss and Kate Winslett.

Once there was a girl called Katie. She lived happily with her parents, brothers and sisters. Katie had lots of friends. She liked to talk to them every day. She was a sweet, kind and helpful little girl. Everyone wanted to be her friend.

Each night she dreamed about her friends and the things that had happened during the day.

Then one night Katie had a very different type of dream. She was talking and laughing with her friends when suddenly someone shouted "Who is that laughing in my castle? I am the only one here who is sweet."

Katie looked around. She was amazed to see a very cross-looking king. She was even more amazed that he was made entirely of chocolate. He had a brown chocolate face, with a white chocolate crown. His coat collar was covered in jelly beans. The buttons were made of marshmallows. His belt was made of dark chocolate. His legs were made of candy cane and, as he walked, toffee sweets fell from holes in his pockets.

"I think you have been eating my sugar, you are too sweet and nice," he said. You see this king was very jealous. He hated people talking to anyone else when he was around.

Katie began chatting with her friends again.

"You're talking to all my friends. It's not fair. They think you're sweeter than me," he shouted, jumping up and down. He became hot and flustered. His crown fell down over one eye.

Suddenly the Choc Ice Queen rushed into the room.

"Cool down," she said, mopping his brow.

Instead it was the Ice Cream Queen who began to melt
and she soon disappeared
into her wrapper.

Now the king suddenly became quiet. He looked at the melted queen. He looked at Katie. Then he said "I have a suggestion. I will make you a princess. I will give you a golden crown with jewels. You can live in a special room in my castle."

He smiled and bowed. He danced a pirouette. He offered her chocolate in gold and silver paper. His servants carried in swings and slides and a merry-go-round for her to play on.

Katie was still annoyed. "No. Thank you," she said. "If I go to live in your castle I will never see my friends again."

On hearing this the king had another tantrum. His face scrunched up and he made another silly face.

Katie jumped on the merry-go-round to have some fun.

"I am going to knock you off your horse," said the king, and he began spinning the merry-go-round faster and faster.

Suddenly he was sent flying high in the air and banged his head on the ceiling. He broke into little pieces and hundreds of chocolate buttons and toffees fell to the floor.

Then Katie woke up. The king and the merry-go-round had disappeared. Her mum and her best friends were beside her bed. "Are you better now? You had a bad fever," said her mum. Katie told her all about her dream, of how the chocolate king had tried to frighten her and trick her into abandoning her friends.

Her mum smiled. "Sometimes people that are too sweet are not as nice as they seem. True friends are the most important treasures of all." she said.

23

What's in a name?

Usually centuries of history, religious or legendary tradition.

The main source of names is in religious history, in the names of saints (Catherine) and, post Reformation, in the *Bible* and *Old Testament* in particular (Sarah and Adam). The *Koran* provides additional perspective on many of these names.

Names from Celtic legend, like Conor, have recently gained increased attention internationally.

Another source is classical, from pagan, royal or literary figures, e.g. Lawrence (Latin) and Chloe (Greek literature). Historical figures, such as Victoria, also provide a rich source.

Then there's Jack! It probably deserves a category all of its own having appeared from nowhere - but perhaps from Jankin, a version of John - to become the ubiquitous name in fairy tales and now a highly popular first name.

Recently parents have become much more adventurous. This follows the decrease in family and religious bonds that resulted in names passing from generation to generation. Increased access to other cultures has led to 'name globalisation', with names like Tanya, Brooklyn and Chelsea now more popular.

Other names recall a particular individual or event. The *Bible* and *Koran* name, Aron, received a new lease of life - and spelling - from Elvis Aaron Presley. Jack